A Note to Parents

For many children, learning math is difficult and "I hate math!" is their first response — to which many parents silently add "Me, too!" Children often see adults comfortably reading and writing, but they rarely have such models for mathematics. And math fear can be catching!

The easy-to-read stories in this **Hello Math Reader!** series were written to give children a positive introduction to mathematics, and parents a pleasurable re-acquaintance with a subject that is important to everyone's life. **Hello Math Reader!** stories make mathematical ideas accessible, interesting, and fun for children. The activities and suggestions at the end of each book provide parents with a hands-on approach to help children develop mathematical interest and confidence.

Enjoy the mathematics!

• Give your child a chance to retell the story. The more familiar children are with the story, the more they will understand its mathematical concepts.

• Use the colorful illustrations to help children "hear and see" the math at work in the story.

• Treat the math activities as games to be played for fun. Follow your child's lead. Spend time on those activities that engage your child's interest and curiosity.

• Activities, especially ones using physical materials, help make abstract mathematical ideas concrete.

Learning is a messy process. Learning about math calls for children to become immersed in lively experiences that help them make sense of mathematical concepts and symbols.

Although learning about numbers is basic to math, other ideas, such as identifying shapes and patterns, measuring, collecting and interpreting data, reasoning logically, and thinking about chance, are also important. By reading these stories and having fun with the activities, you will help your child enthusiastically say "**Hello, math**," instead of "I hate math."

—Marilyn Burns
National Mathematics Educator
Author of *The I Hate Mathematics! Book*

For my heavenly Father
and for Bruce, Seth, Tim,
Andrea, and Jasmine.
— C.N.

To my four-year-old daughter
Flynn, who helps me pick our
tomatoes whether they're
red or green.
— T.S.

ISBN 0-439-16967-4

Copyright © 2001 by Scholastic Inc.
The activities on pages 43-48 copyright © 2001 by Marilyn Burns.
All rights reserved. Published by Scholastic Inc.
SCHOLASTIC, HELLO MATH READER, CARTWHEEL BOOKS and associated logos are trademarks and/or registered trademarks of Scholastic Inc.

Library of Congress Cataloging-in-Publication Data

Neuschwander, Cindy.
    88 pounds of tomatoes/ by Cindy Neuschwander; illustrated by Terry Sirrell; math activities by Marilyn Burns.
        p.   cm. — (Hello reader! Math. Level 4)
    Summary: Two friends plan a party to use all the tomatoes they expect to get from their Wonder Plant.
        ISBN 0-439-16967-4
        [1. Measurement — Fiction.   2. Word problems (Mathematics) — Fiction. 3. Tomatoes — Fiction.]   I. Title: 88 pounds of tomatoes.   II. Sirrell, Terry, ill. III. Burns, Marilyn, IV. Title V. Series.
        PZ7.N4453 Ei 2001
        [E]—dc21   00-029662

10 9 8 7 6 5 4 3 2   02 03 04 05 06

Printed in the U.S.A.   23
First printing, February 2001

88 Pounds of Tomatoes

by Cindy Neuschwander 🍃 Illustrated by Terry Sirrell
Math Activities by Marilyn Burns

Hello Math Reader! — Level 4

Cartwheel
·B·O·O·K·S·®
SCHOLASTIC INC.
New York Toronto London Auckland Sydney
Mexico City New Delhi Hong Kong

My dad walks in from work.

"Hello! Hello!" he says. "I've got 88 pounds of tomatoes!"

"That looks like a tiny plant to me," I say.

"Listen to this." My dad reads aloud: "The Wonder Plant grows up to six feet tall. Get 88 pounds of tomatoes after ten weeks from just one plant!"

"What in the world would we do with 88 pounds of tomatoes?" asks my mom.

"We could have a neighborhood party," suggests my dad.

"We could make spaghetti, pizza, and tomato salad!" I add.

"You and your dad have wild ideas!" my mom laughs.

I think we have great ideas.

I run next door and get my good friend Katie. I show her the Wonder Plant.

"Eighty-eight pounds of tomatoes from *this*?" asks Katie. "Mack, you are dreaming."

We take the tomato plant. We put it in a big pot. We water it.

"Let's make up invitations for a Wonder Plant party," I say.

"Shouldn't we wait until there are some tomatoes?" asks Katie.

"There will be lots of tomatoes," I answer.

Together, we make 12 invitations. There is one for every family on our street, including our own. Katie and I walk up and down the street. We put the invitations in 12 mailboxes.

That night, I dream about tomatoes. The Wonder Plant grows high into the sky. I climb up, up, up. A giant chases me! I scramble down, down, down. I wake up thinking I am Mack and the Green Stalk.

The next day, Katie comes over. She has a handful of invitations.

"Look, Mack!" she says. "All these families are coming to the Wonder Plant party."

I have 3 invitations. Katie has 5 more than I do. We sent out 12 invitations and 11 have been returned. That means 1 family has not sent back its invitation. I wonder who it is. I do not wonder very long.

"Mack!" calls my mom. "What is this?" She flaps around our invitation.

"It's an invitation to the Wonder Plant party," I say. "Eleven families will be here. I hope we are coming because it is at our house."

"Mack, we can't have this party without lots of tomatoes!" my mom says.

"Don't worry," I tell her. "We have the Wonder Plant!"

Even though our Wonder Plant party is not for several weeks, Katie and I want to make plans. We start with the guest list.

"Eight families are coming with five people each," I say.

"That's 40 people," Katie tells me, "including my family."

"There will also be three families of four people," I tell her.

"That's 12 people," Katie answers. "Don't forget you and your family, Mack. That will be 3 more."

"Altogether there are 55 people coming to our Wonder Plant party," I say. "But 5 are babies, so they won't eat much. We need enough food for 50 people. That's a lot of food."

"That's a lot of tomatoes!" says Katie.

Katie pulls out a cookbook. She looks up spaghetti. "One pound of tomatoes cooks down to one cup of sauce," she reads aloud. "Use one cup of sauce for each person." Katie looks at our list. "That's 50 cups of spaghetti sauce," she says.

"That's 50 pounds of tomatoes," I say. "If we have 88 pounds of tomatoes from the Wonder Plant, we can use 50 pounds for the spaghetti sauce and still have 38 pounds of tomatoes left over."

"Mack," Katie reminds me, "we don't have any pounds of tomatoes."

"Don't worry," I say. "We will have plenty of tomatoes. Now let's look for a pizza recipe."

Katie and I flip through the cookbook. We find the pizza recipe. The first step says: "See spaghetti sauce. Use one cup per pizza."

"This is easy," I say. "Another 30 pounds of tomatoes should make enough pizza sauce for 30 pizzas. Thirty pizzas should be plenty for 50 people. So, if there are 38 pounds of tomatoes left after the spaghetti, we can subtract 30 pounds for the pizza. We will still have 8 pounds of tomatoes left for the salad."

I am very pleased with our party plans. I don't know why Katie is so worried. The tomatoes will grow.

We keep watering and checking our Wonder Plant. After four weeks, it is much taller but there are still no tomatoes.

"Maybe our plant is unhappy," I say.

"Let's tell it a joke," suggests Katie.

"If you have seven tomatoes in one hand and eight tomatoes in the other hand, what do you have?" I ask the Wonder Plant.

"Big hands!" Katie tells it.

Katie and I crack up. I am not sure if tomato plants can laugh, but I think the plant is happy, too. Soon there are small green tomatoes all over it.

Katie and I keep making party plans.

I take a look at the plant label. "Tomatoes grow in 10 weeks," I read.

"Our plant has been growing for 4 weeks," Katie says.

"That means we have 6 more weeks to wait. Then we can pick the tomatoes," I say.

"We will need to weigh them," says Katie. "Otherwise, how will we know if we have enough tomatoes for the spaghetti sauce, the pizza sauce, and the salad!"

"No problem," I tell her. "We can use our bathroom scale."

"Interesting," says Katie, when she sees
our scale.

Our scale is shaped like a pig.

"I'll show you how it works," I say.

I grab my dog, Ima Mutt. I put her on the
scale.

"Oink-oink," the scale says to Ima. "You
weigh 30 pounds."

Ima jumps off and runs away. She does
not like being oinked at.

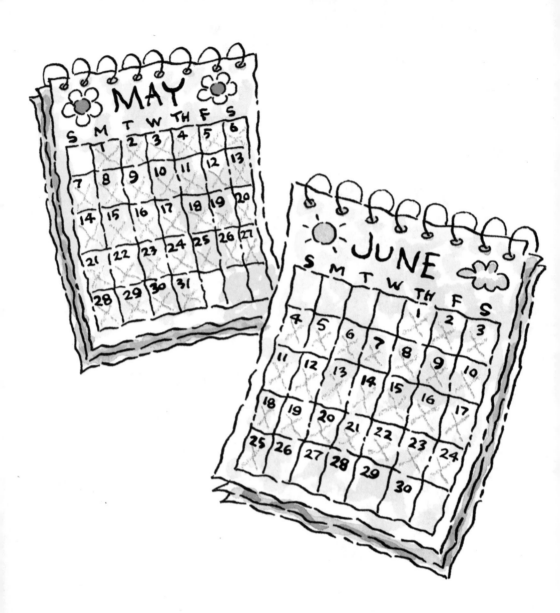

Four weeks later, the green tomatoes are bigger. We tell our plant another joke to help them along.

"Why did the tomato turn red?" Katie asks the Wonder Plant. "Because it saw the salad dressing!" I answer. We both laugh.

In two more weeks, some of the tomatoes have turned red. We pick them. We carry them into the bathroom and put them on the scale.

"Oink-oink," the scale says to the tomatoes. "You weigh ten pounds."

"We need 88 pounds," I say. "We have 10 pounds. How many more pounds have to grow?"

"88 pounds minus 10 pounds is 78 more pounds," says Katie. "That's a lot of tomatoes!"

"Don't worry!" I tell her.

OINK-OINK!
You WEIGH
10 POUNDS.

The next few days are very sunny. We check the Wonder Plant again. There are many ripe tomatoes. We pick them. We pull them into the bathroom in my wagon. We stack them on the scale.

"Oink-oink. You weigh 30 pounds," says the scale. We subtract that from the 78 pounds we still need. We have 48 pounds to go.

After we pick another 30 pounds, Katie says, "Only 18 more pounds to pick! Maybe we will have enough tomatoes for the Wonder Plant party."

"Of course we will," I say.

Tomatoes are piling up in our kitchen. The sink is overflowing with them. Our kitchen table is covered with them. Tomatoes are stacked on the windowsills and rolling off the countertops.

"Mack," says my mom, "we need to make the spaghetti and pizza sauce before all that's left here is ketchup."

"Sure," I tell her. "But first Katie and I have to check the Wonder Plant."

Katie and I race outside to pick tomatoes. We race inside to weigh them. This time there are only 10 pounds of juicy red tomatoes. We subtract these from the 18 pounds we need. We still have 8 pounds to go. But the Wonder Plant is slowing up.

Katie and I look at each other. "A joke!" we say at the same time. We head for the Wonder Plant.

I begin. "Why did the tomato stop running?"

Katie answers. "It ran out of juice." We smile and say to our plant, "We hope you are not running out of juice."

We go in and help my mom. This is fun! We mash the tomatoes until they are all squishy. We are up to our elbows in dribbley, juicy tomatoes. When the tomatoes are all mashed, my mom cooks them in a huge pot to make the sauce.

On Wonder Plant party day, we set up tables in our backyard. We set 55 places, but we only put silverware at 50. "The babies won't need knives and forks," I say, "but they might need seats." My mom and dad cook the pizzas and the spaghetti. Katie and I are in charge of the salad.

"Let's go pick tomatoes for the salad," I say.

On our way over to the Wonder Plant, we run into Ima Mutt. Her face is red and gooey. She has tomato seeds on her nose. She is licking her mouth. She has a big doggy smile.

"Oh, no!" I cry out. "Ima has eaten tomatoes off of our plant! Now we will never know if our Wonder Plant really grew 88 pounds of tomatoes!"

Katie smiles a big smarty smile. "Let's weigh Ima again, now that she's full of tomatoes. Then we can subtract her weight without tomatoes."

"Good idea," I say.

We pick up Ima. We put her on the
pig scale.

"Oink-oink," it says to her. "You weigh
38 pounds."

"She weighed 30 pounds before," Katie
remembers, "and 38 minus 30 is 8. Ima! You
ate eight pounds of tomatoes?" Ima wags
her tail.

I stop and think. "The Wonder Plant made
it!" I say. "It grew 88 pounds of tomatoes!
Those were the last eight pounds we
needed!"

"Uh-oh," Katie says. "Now our salad tomatoes are inside Ima."

"We will just have a green salad," I tell Katie. "A *very* green salad. Let's hurry, people are already here."

Everyone loves the Wonder Plant party.
Everything, the spaghetti, the pizzas, even
the very green salad, gets eaten up.
"*Wonderful* party," I say to Katie. We
crack up.

The next day, Katie and I sit around.
There are no tomatoes to pick. Then I spot
something red.

"Katie!" I say. "Look!"

"Here, Ima, here girl," Katie calls.

Ima Mutt takes care of it.

• ABOUT THE ACTIVITIES •

Learning about measurement is an important part of learning mathematics. Measurement is a practical aspect of math that helps children see how math can be useful, and it gives them experience using math skills to solve real-world problems. Also, measurement experiences provide contexts for numbers, helping children see how numbers are used in various situations and motivating them to reason numerically.

88 Pounds of Tomatoes is a delightfully wacky story about two friends, Mack and Katie, and what they did with an extraordinary tomato plant. The story encourages children to think about measuring time, height, and weight as Mack and Katie make plans to cook spaghetti sauce for a neighborhood feast.

It's not only valuable for your child to learn to think and reason in their heads, but also to use tools to solve problems. You'll see that some of the activities in this section ask your child to reason numerically, while others ask that he or she use measuring tools such as rulers, yardsticks, a calendar, the bathroom scale, and even string. In all the activities, it's important to encourage your child to communicate about his or her reasoning and for you to listen to the explanations. Talking about their thinking is enormously helpful for supporting children's learning of mathematics.

Enjoy the story with your child and have fun with math!

—Marilyn Burns

You'll find tips and suggestions
for guiding the activities whenever
you see a box like this!

Retelling the Story

Dad read: "The Wonder Plant grows up to six feet tall." Do you know anyone who is about six feet tall?

Dad also read: "Get 88 pounds of tomatoes after 10 weeks." If Dad planted it today, what date would be 10 weeks from now? (A calendar can help you figure.)

Mack and Katie sent out 12 invitations. Mack received 3 back and Katie received 5 more than Mack did. Can you explain why that means they received 11 invitations back all together?

> Understanding how "more than" is used is difficult for children. If your child thinks that Mack and Katie should have only eight invitations, or arrives at another incorrect answer, help make the problem concrete by using slips of paper to represent the invitations.

Eight families with five people each, and three families with four people each are coming to the party. How many people does that make all together? How did you figure it out?

Mack and Katie figured that even though 55 people would be coming, they only had to cook for 50. Why did they think that?

One pound of tomatoes makes one cup of sauce for spaghetti. That means 88 pounds makes 88 cups of sauce. But Mack and Katie only need to make 50 cups. How many extra pounds of tomatoes will they have?

What do Mack and Katie plan to do with the extra tomatoes?

After four weeks, there are still no tomatoes. What joke does Mack tell the Wonder Plant? How many more weeks until the tomatoes are ready?

Four weeks later, Katie tells the Wonder Plant a joke. What was it? Now how many more weeks until the tomatoes are ready?

Two weeks later, there are 10 pounds of tomatoes. How many more pounds do Mack and Katie need?

After a few sunny days, Mack and Katie picked 30 more pounds of tomatoes. And then they picked 30 more pounds. Katie says, "Only 18 more pounds to pick." How did Katie figure this out?

The next time Katie and Mack pick tomatoes, they pick 10 more pounds. They subtract this from the 18 pounds they still need. How many pounds are there to go? What joke did Mack tell now to the Wonder Plant?

What happened to the last eight pounds of tomatoes?

Six Feet of String

The Wonder Plant grows up to six feet tall. Measure six feet on the floor and cut a piece of string that long. Here are some ways you can do this:

Get six rulers that are each one foot long and lay them end to end.

If you only have one ruler, mark a starting place and then move it along six times.

Use a yardstick. It measures three feet. Two yardstick lengths make six feet.

String Measures

Now use your string to measure each of the things below to see which is more than six feet, less than six feet, or just about six feet.

How tall is the refrigerator?

How long is your bed?

How tall is the front door?

How far is it across your bedroom?

How far is it across the kitchen table?

How long is the bathtub?

How long is the family car or your bicycle?

Find some other things to measure.

From Feet to Inches

There are 12 inches in a foot. There are 36 inches in 3 feet. How many inches are there in 6 feet?

About how many inches tall are you?

About how many feet tall are you?

Bathroom Scale Weighing

Mack and Katie use the bathroom scale to weigh the tomatoes. Use the bathroom scale to find out how much you weigh.

If you were holding some things that weighed five pounds, then what would the scale read? Find some things that weigh five pounds and check.

What if you were holding things that weighed 10 pounds? Try it.